Dinosaurs Sticker Book

Dr. David Norman

Illustrated by Bob Hersey, Ian Jackson,
Todd Marshall, Luis Rey, Franco Tempesta,
John Woodcock and David Wright

Edited by Sarah Khan
Designed by Reuben Barrance
Consultant: Darren Naish

How to use this book

There are over eighty dinosaurs and prehistoric animals in this book. Using the descriptions and the pictures, match each sticker to the right animal. A checklist and index at the back of the book tells you which sticker goes with which description.

A pronunciation guide is given for the names of most of the animals. You can also hear how to say their names on the Usborne Quicklinks Website. Just go to www.usborne-quicklinks.com and type in the keywords **dinosaur names**.

There is a head-to-tail measurement of each creature, and the period in which it lived. Below, you can see when these periods were ("mya" stands for "millions of years ago").

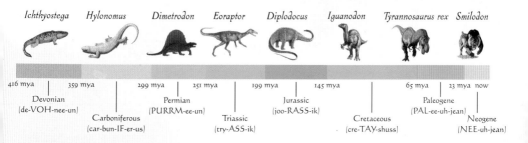

| Ichthyostega | Hylonomus | Dimetrodon | Eoraptor | Diplodocus | Iguanodon | Tyrannosaurus rex | Smilodon |

| 416 mya | | 359 mya | | 299 mya | | 251 mya | | 199 mya | | 145 mya | | | 65 mya | | 23 mya | now |
| Devonian (de-VOH-nee-un) | | | Carboniferous (car-bun-IF-er-us) | | Permian (PURRM-ee-un) | | Triassic (try-ASS-ik) | | Jurassic (joo-RASS-ik) | | Cretaceous (cre-TAY-shuss) | | Paleogene (PAL-ee-uh-jean) | | Neogene (NEE-uh-jean) | |

Before the dinosaurs

Millions of years before the dinosaurs, all animals lived in the water. Over many generations, their bodies changed and some began to live on the land.

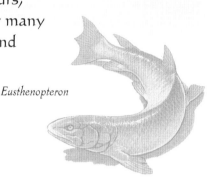

Eusthenopteron

Ichthyostega

Ichthyostega

(ik-thee-OS-tig-a)

An amphibian (lived on dry land some of the time, but returned to the water to lay their squashy eggs). Ate fish. 1m (3ft) long. Late Devonian.

Eusthenopteron

(use-then-OP-ter-on)

Fish. Lived around 375 million years ago. Crawled onto land when water dried up in hot seasons. Sharp teeth. Strong fins to help it swim and pull itself along the ground. 1m (3ft) long. Devonian.

Seymouria

Diplocaulus

Diplocaulus

(dip-lo-CALL-us)

Spent most of its life in water. Flat body. Boomerang-shaped head may have stabilized it when in fast-flowing streams. 80cm (2ft) long. Permian.

Seymouria

(see-MORE-ee-a)

Lived mainly on dry land. Fairly powerful legs. One of a range of early land animals. 80cm (2ft) long. Permian.

Dinosaur ancestors

The ancestors of the dinosaurs were reptiles called archosaurs (ARK-o-saurs). Reptiles have scaly skin, and lay eggs on land.

Pareiasaurus

Hylonomus

Pareiasaurus

(pa-ray-a-SORE-us)

Plant-eater. Solid build with a tough hide. Bony bumps and knobs on head. May have been an ancestor to modern turtles. 2.5m (8¼ft) long. Permian.

Hylonomus

(high-LON-om-us)

Small and lizard-like. One of the earliest reptiles scientists know about. Strong ribs and lungs for breathing air. 20cm (8in) long. Carboniferous.

Euparkeria

(you-park-EAR-ee-a)

Euparkeria

The size of a cat. Back studded with small, bony plates for protection. Could probably sprint quickly on its back legs. 70cm (27½in) long. Early Triassic.

Rutiodon

Rutiodon

(ROOT-ee-o-don)

Crocodile-like archosaur. Nostrils on raised mound between its eyes. Lived in water. Fed mostly on fish. 4–5m (13–16½ft) long. Late Triassic.

Sharovipteryx

Sharovipteryx

(sha-rov-IP-ter-ix)

Probably lived in trees. May have glided using the skin stretched between its tail and back legs. 20cm (8in) long. Triassic.

Tyrannosaurus rex

Big hunters

Theropods (THAIR-op-odds) were a group of meat-eating dinosaurs that moved on two legs. The largest ones probably used their teeth, rather than their claws, to kill their prey.

Allosaurus

(al-o-SORE-us)

Large theropod. Hunted giant sauropods*. Scientists know this because they found the teeth marks of *Allosaurus* embedded in an *Apatosaurus* skeleton. 10m (33ft) long. Late Jurassic.

Allosaurus

Tyrannosaurus rex

(tih-ran-o-SORE-us rex)

One of the biggest land predators that has ever lived. Massive head. Powerful jaws to crush prey. Name means "tyrant lizard king" in Latin. Many scientists think it was a relative of modern birds. Young may have had downy feathers. 5m (16½ft) tall. 12m (40ft) long. Late Cretaceous.

Ceratosaurus

(se-rat-o-SORE-us)

Row of small, bony plates along back. Bony ridges over eyes. Horn on snout, which may have been used by the males for butting each other. 6m (19½ft) long. Late Jurassic.

Ceratosaurus

* You can find out about sauropods on page 9.

Majungatholus

(mah-joong-ga-THO-lus)

Theropod whose remains have
been found in Madagascar, off the
coast of Africa. Hunted plant-eaters
such as sauropods*. Also seems to have
been a cannibal, feeding on its own
kind. 8m (26ft) long. Late Cretaceous.

Majungatholus

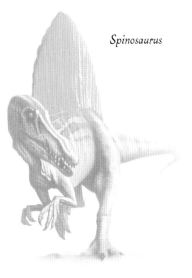

Spinosaurus

Spinosaurus

(spy-no-SORE-us)

Had spines making a sort of "sail" on its
back. Some spines were up to 2m (6½ft) long.
This sail may have helped to control the
dinosaur's temperature by allowing it to gain
or lose heat. Some scientists think it wasn't
a sail but a fatty hump, like a bison's, storing
energy for times when food was scarce.
15m (50ft) long. Cretaceous.

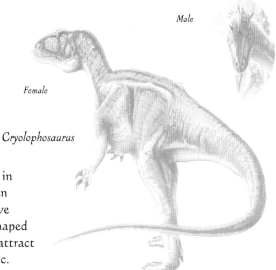

Male

Female

Cryolophosaurus

Cryolophosaurus

(cry-oh-lof-o-SORE-us)

An *Allosaurus*-like theropod. Lived in
Antarctica, which was warmer then
than now, though it would still have
been very cold. Males had a fan-shaped
crest which they probably used to attract
mates. 7m (23ft) long. Early Jurassic.

Fast runners

Some meat-eating dinosaurs ran at high speeds to chase their prey and escape the larger meat-eaters.

Compsognathus

Velociraptor

Velociraptor

(ve-LOSS-i-rap-ter)

Probably feathered. Long, curved claw on each foot, which it probably used to grip prey and pierce its windpipe. 1.5m (5ft) long. Late Cretaceous.

Eoraptor

Eoraptor

(EE-oh-rap-ter)

One of the earliest known dinosaurs. Small, fast-moving theropod. Three fingers on each hand. 1m (3ft) long. Late Triassic.

Compsognathus

(comp-sog-NAITH-us)

One of the smallest known dinosaurs, no bigger than a cat. Chased tiny animals, mainly lizards, for food. Used its long tail to balance when running. Three clawed fingers on each hand. 70cm (27½in) long. Late Jurassic.

Troodon

(TROH-o-don)

Long-legged and bird-like. Large, forward-facing eyes. May have been the most intelligent of all dinosaurs, judging by the size of its brain compared to its body. 1.8m (6ft) long. Late Cretaceous.

Troodon

Coelophysis

Coelophysis

(see-lof-EYE-sis)

One of the early meat-eating dinosaurs. Slender and lightly built, with bird-like feet. Probably lived in groups. Fed on young dinosaurs or small lizards. 3m (10ft) long. Late Triassic.

Megaraptor

Megaraptor attacking an Iguanadon

(MEG-a-rap-ter)

Deadly 40cm (16in) sickle claws. A relative of *Allosaurus*. 8m (26ft) long. Late Cretaceous.

Gallimimus

(ga-li-MY-mus)

Very fast. Ostrich-shaped. Long, toothless beak which it probably used to clip leaves from trees. Long and powerful back legs may have been used for kicking enemies. 6m (20ft) long. Late Cretaceous.

Sinosauropteryx

Sinosauropteryx

(sine-oh-sore-OP-ter-ix)

Remains found in China in 1996. Looked like *Compsognathus*, but covered in fluff or fuzz, which may be early version of feather-like covering. 65cm (25in) long. Early Cretaceous.

Gallimimus

More fast runners

Saurornithoides

(sore-or-nith-OI-deez)

Large eyes. May have seen better in the dark than other dinosaurs. Experts think it may have hunted small, shrew-like mammals that came out at night. 2–3m (6½–10ft) long. Late Cretaceous.

Deinocheirus arms compared in size to an adult human

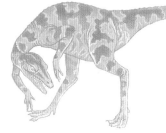

Saurornithoides

Deinocheirus

(dine-o-KY-rus)

So far, only a pair of massive arms has been found. Thought to have been ostrich-like, like a giant *Gallimimus*. Arms 2.4m (8ft) long. Length unknown, but possibly up to 20m (66ft). Late Cretaceous.

Oviraptor

(OH-vi-rap-ter)

Name is Latin for "egg-thief", because first fossil was found lying on top of eggs. It's now thought that the eggs were its own, and that *Oviraptor* was a caring mother. 2.5m (8ft) long. Late Cretaceous.

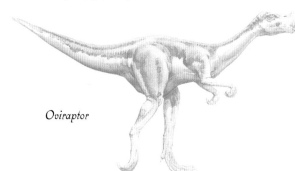

Deinonychus

Oviraptor

Deinonychus

(dine-ON-ih-kus)

Fierce, intelligent hunter. Ambushed its prey, stabbing with claws on back feet. May have hunted in packs. 3m (10ft) long. Early Cretaceous.

Giant plant-eaters

Apatosaurus

Sauropod dinosaurs were plant-eaters with long necks and tails, that lived in the Jurassic and Cretaceous periods. They were the biggest land animals that ever existed.

Diplodocus

Diplodocus

(dih-PLOD-o-kus)

Lightly built. Used whip-like tail to ward off attackers. Long neck helped it to eat treetop leaves. Sharp thumb-claw probably used for fighting. 27m (88½ft) long. Late Jurassic.

Brachiosaurus

Supersaurus

(super-SORE-us)

One of the very largest sauropods. May have been the longest land animal that ever lived. Weighed nearly 50 tonnes (55 tons). 40m (130ft) long. Late Jurassic.

Apatosaurus

(a-pat-o-SORE-us)

Shorter than *Diplodocus*, but much heavier, perhaps weighing as much as about 30 tonnes (33 tons). Used to be known as *Brontosaurus*. 20m (65½ft) long. Late Jurassic.

Brachiosaurus

(brack-ee-o-SORE-us)

Front legs longer than back ones, unlike other sauropods. Long neck to help it feed on tall trees. May have breathed by letting out hot air from nostrils on top of bump on head. 23m (75½ft) long. Late Jurassic.

Supersaurus

Agile plant-eaters

Heterodontosaurus

Ornithopods were plant-eating dinosaurs, whose speed and agility helped them escape predators. They gathered plants or pulled down branches with their short arms, and used their tough beaks to bite shoots and leaves. Their remains have been found in rocks from the Late Triassic to the Early Cretaceous periods.

Hypsilophodon

Hypsilophodon

(hips-ill-OFF-o-don)

Short arms with five fingers on each. Four toes on each foot. Probably used its long, stiff tail to balance while running. Similar small, beaked dinosaurs existed the entire time dinosaurs lived. 2m (6½ft) long. Early Cretaceous.

Heterodontosaurus

(het-er-oh-dont-o-SORE-us)

Distantly related to ornithopods. Strong arms and sharp claws. Tusks in both jaws, may have been used for digging up roots, warding off enemies, or displaying in the mating season. 1m (3¼ft) long. Early Jurassic.

Leaellynasaura

(lee-ell-in-a-SORE-a)

Small ornithopod with long legs. Lived in Australia, which was colder then than now. Very likely lived in groups. Big eyes, which would have helped it see in dim winter months. 2.5m (8ft) long. Early Cretaceous.

Leaellynasaura

Iguanodon

Iguanodon

(ig-WAN-o-don)

Beak. Powerful tail and back
legs. Long pointed spike on each
thumb, which it probably used to
defend itself. Hoof-like claws on
other fingers, so it could walk on
all fours if necessary. 10m (33ft)
long. Early Cretaceous.

Early idea of an
Iguanodon

Iguanodon discoveries

Iguanodon teeth and bones were
discovered first. Experts thought
that they might belong to a huge,
scaly rhinoceros-like dinosaur, with
a bone on its nose. When complete
skeletons were found later, they realized
that this bone was really a thumb-claw.

Muttaburrasaurus

(muht-a-buhr-a-SORE-us)

From Australia. A close relative of
Iguanodon. Males may have had large
bumps on their muzzles, with bright
markings to attract mates. 7m (23ft)
long. Early Cretaceous.

Muttaburrasaurus

Male   Female

Ouranosaurus

(oo-ran-o-SORE-us)

A close relative of *Iguanodon*, but
had a broad, flattened beak. Sail-
like crest on its back helped control
its body temperature. As with the
Spinosaurus, this may have supported
a fatty hump. 6m (19½ft)
long. Cretaceous.

Ouranosaurus

Duck-billed dinosaurs

Duck-billed dinosaurs, also known as hadrosaurs, had top jaws with flattened tips that looked like a duck's beak. Many had spikes or crests on their heads, which may have helped them to make noises to alert others to danger, warn off enemies or to call mates.

Hadrosaurus

Tsintaosaurus

(ching-dow-SORE-us)

Remains found in China. Seems to have had long, solid bone head spike that pointed forwards, and possibly supported flaps of skin. Hundreds of tiny teeth for grinding up tough plants. 10m (33ft) long. Late Cretaceous.

Hadrosaurus

(had-ro-SORE-us)

First dinosaur with a near-complete skeleton to be found. Ate leaves from bushes. 10m (33ft) long. Late Cretaceous.

Parasaurolophus

Tsintaosaurus

Parasaurolophus

(para-sore-OL-o-fuss)

Amazing crest made of long, curved, tube-shaped bone. May have blown air through the crest to make trombone-like noises. 10m (33ft) long. Late Cretaceous.

1

2

3

4

5

6

7

8

9

10

11

13

12

14

15

16

17

18

19

20

21

23

22

25

24

28

26

27

29

30

31

32

33

34

35

36

37

38

39

40

41

42

43

44

45

46

47

48

49

50

51

52

53

54

55

56

57

58

59

60

61

62

63

64

65

66

67

68

69

70

71

81

82

83

84

87

85

86

88

Edmontosaurus

Saurolophus

(sore-OL-o-fuss)

Backward-pointing prong on head, possibly a support for nose pouches. May have blown up the pouches with air, to bellow at rivals. 13m (40ft) long. Late Cretaceous.

Edmontosaurus

(ed-mont-o-SORE-us)

Roamed in forests and lived in groups for protection. Fed on plants and, despite large size, could run quickly on strong back legs. 10m (33ft) long. Late Cretaceous.

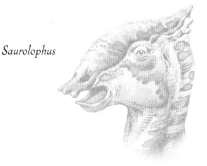

Saurolophus

Corythosaurus

Kritosaurus

(krit-o-SORE-us)

Flat head with rounded hump on nose. Males may have used this for head-butting rivals. Females may not have had this hump. 10m (33ft) long. Late Cretaceous.

Corythosaurus

(ko-rith-o-SORE-us)

Name means "helmet lizard" and refers to the shape of its crest. This had many hollow passages inside, running from the tip of the dinosaur's nose to the back of its throat. Some experts believe that the passages gave *Corythosaurus* a strong sense of smell, or helped it make trumpet-like sounds. 10m (33ft) long. Late Cretaceous.

Kritosaurus

Fossil clues

Knowledge about prehistoric life comes from fossils of animals and plants that died millions of years ago.

Ichthyosaurus skeleton

(ik-thee-o-SORE-us)

This fossil *Ichthyosaurus* is very well preserved. Even the outline of its skin can be seen. 1.8m (6ft) long. Jurassic.

Ichthyosaurus skeleton

Maiasaura

(my-a-SORE-a)

Maiasaura guarding its young

Nests made of mud, with fossilized eggs and baby dinosaurs, were discovered in Montana, USA. Nests belonged to a hadrosaur, called *Maiasaura*, which looked after its eggs and fed its babies with berries. 9m (30ft) long. Cretaceous.

Dinosaur skin

Fossilized impressions of dinosaur skin show that some dinosaurs had pebbly skin. Soft tissue has rotted away, so no one knows for certain what real skin shades were.

Dinosaur skin

Dinosaur dropping

Fossil eggs

Dinosaur nests found in Mongolia contained eggs that were 15–20cm (6–8in) long. Possibly belonged to *Oviraptor*. Each female laid up to twelve eggs in the sand, in a circle.

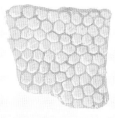

Fossil eggs

Dinosaur dropping

Fossilized droppings are called coprolites. Scientists cut them into thin slices and examine them under a microscope. They can show what dinosaurs ate and also the shape of the dinosaur's intestines.

Bone-headed dinosaurs

Pachycephalosaurs (pak-ee-SEFA-lo-saws) are described as bone-headed because of their very thick skulls.

Stegoceras

Male Pachycephalosaurs

Stegoceras

(steg-OS-er-as)

The first bone-head ever to be found. Cluster of bumps around back and sides of head. May have lived in herds. 3m (10ft) long. Late Cretaceous.

Battling bone-heads

Males probably charged at each other, head-butting rivals' bodies. They would do this again and again until one gave up. The winner became leader of the herd.

Pachycephalosaurus

Homalocephale

Homalocephale

(hom-a-low-SEF-al-ee)

Very well-preserved fossils discovered in Mongolia. Unusually flat skull, with bony knobs at the sides. Name means "level head". Stiff, thick tail. 2.5m (8ft) long. Late Cretaceous.

Pachycephalosaurus

(pak-ee-sefa-low-SORE-us)

Biggest bone-headed dinosaur. Had the largest bony, dome-shaped head. Skull much bumpier than *Stegoceras* (below). Lumps and spikes on its nose. 8m (26ft) long. Late Cretaceous.

Horned dinosaurs

Ceratopsians (sera-TOPS-ee-ans) were mostly large and heavy, with horns on their heads, a bony frill around their necks, and parrot-like beaks.

Pentaceratops

Monoclonius

Pentaceratops

(pent-ah-SERA-tops)

Large frill extending halfway down its back. Nose and eyebrow horns, and pointed cheekbones beneath eyes. 7m (23ft) long. Late Cretaceous.

Protoceratops grappling with Velociraptor

Protoceratops

(proh-toe-SERA-tops)

Ancestor of horned dinosaurs such as *Monoclonius* and *Pentaceratops*. Strong beak for eating tough plants. One Mongolian fossil shows *Pentaceratops* fighting *Velociraptor*. 2m (6½ft) long. Cretaceous.

Monoclonius

(mon-o-CLONE-ee-us)

From the side, looked similar to a modern-day rhinoceros. One bony horn on nose. Very small eyebrow ridges. 8m (26ft) long. Late Cretaceous.

Living in herds

Many *Monoclonius* fossils have been found lying together. Experts think that at least some of the horned dinosaurs lived in herds. They may also have surrounded their babies to protect them from enemies when threatened. However, there is not yet any solid evidence to support this idea.

Monoclonius protecting their young

Pachyrhinosaurus

(pack-ee-rye-no-SORE-us)

Short frill and no obvious horns.
Thick, flattened pad instead of
pointed nose horn. Only a few
skulls found so far. 4m (13ft)
long. Late Cretaceous.

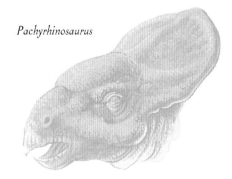

Pachyrhinosaurus

Psittacosaurus

(sit-ak-o-SORE-us)

Similar shape to ornithopods.
Unusually for a ceratopsian,
walked on its back legs, although
probably walked on all fours
at times. 2m (6½ft) long.
Cretaceous.

Psittacosaurus

Triceratops

Triceratops

(try-SERA-tops)

Sharp horns around eyes grew up to
1.5m (5ft) long. Probably charged head-
down at enemies, spearing them to
death. One of the largest and also one
of the last horned dinosaurs. 11m (36ft)
long. Late Cretaceous.

Leptoceratops

Leptoceratops

(lep-toe-SERA-tops)

Small and agile, unlike other
ceratopsians. Ran on all fours to escape
enemies, so no need for horns to defend
itself. Little frill around neck. 2m (6½ft)
long. Late Cretaceous.

Spikes and bony backs

Stegosaurs had bony plates sticking out of their backs. Ankylosaurs were protected by spikes and bony shields.

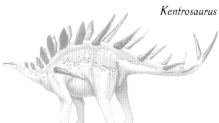
Kentrosaurus

Stegosaurus

Stegosaurus

(steg-o-SORE-us)

Experts think it displayed the large plates on its back to attract mates or warn enemies. Cluster of sharp spikes on tail for protection. 8m (26ft) long. Late Jurassic.

Polacanthus

(pol-a-KANTH-us)

Ankylosaur with broad, shield-like band of bony plating across hips, and double row of spines along neck and tail. 4m (13ft) long. Cretaceous.

Polacanthus

Kentrosaurus

(kent-ro-SORE-us)

Long spike on each side of body, as well as rows of spikes along back. Probably turned its back on enemies to make an attack difficult. 5m (16½ft) long. Late Jurassic.

Scelidosaurus

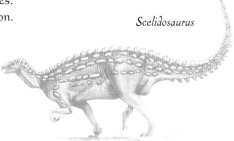

Scelidosaurus

(ske-lid-o-SORE-us)

Early ankylosaur. Turtle-like beak for close nibbling of low-lying plants. The first near-complete fossil dinosaur discovered, in Dorset, England, in 1858. 4m (13ft) long. Early Jurassic.

Ankylosaurus

(ank-eye-lo-SORE-us)

Thick, flexible, bony plates over head, neck and back. Chunks of bone on end of tail form a club. When under attack, it probably crouched down to protect its soft belly and swung its tail into its enemy's legs. 4.5m (15ft) long. Late Cretaceous.

Panoplosaurus

Panoplosaurus

(pan-o-plo-SORE-us)

Ankylosaur with simple, leaf-shaped teeth, similar to stegosaurs. Jaw ended in tough, toothless beak. Spikes along sides. 7m (30ft) long. Late Cretaceous.

Ankylosaurus

Euoplocephalus

Nodosaurus

(node-o-SORE-us)

Name means "knobbly lizard". Ankylosaur with broad bands of rounded, bony lumps across its back. Thick, heavy coat acted as protective plating. 6m (19½ft) long. Cretaceous.

Nodosaurus

Euoplocephalus

(you-oh-plo-SEF-a-lus)

Large ankylosaur. Heavy, bony plating on skin with bumps and lumps growing out of it. Thick, helmet-like pad of bone covered head. Eyelids shielded by bony plates. Belly appears to have been soft and unprotected. 7m (23ft) long. Late Cretaceous.

Flying reptiles

Flying reptiles called pterosaurs (TEH-ro-saws) had leathery wings and may have been covered with hairy fuzz.

Pterodactylus

Pterodaustro

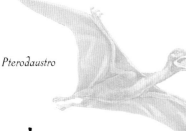

Pterodaustro

(teh-ro-DAW-stroh)

South American. Long, curved beak. Used tightly packed, bristle-like teeth to filter tiny creatures from the sea. 1.3m (4¼ft) long. Early Cretaceous.

Pteranodon

Pteranodon

(teh-RAN-o-don)

Huge wings and short, stumpy tail. Light, hollow bones to help it fly. Long, bony crest on head. No teeth, but may have had pelican-like pouch to carry fish it snatched. 1.8m (6ft) long. Late Cretaceous.

Pterodactylus

(teh-ro-DAK-til-us)

Very small and fast-moving. May have snapped insects out of the air as it flew, or probed for worms in shallow water. Would have crouched on all fours when landing on the ground. 20cm (8in) long. Late Jurassic.

Rhamphorhynchus

(ram-for-RINK-us)

Sharp beak on jaw-tips and sharp, forward-pointing teeth to help grasp fish. Kite-shaped tip of long tail helped it steer as it skimmed the sea's surface for prey. 30cm (12in) long. Late Jurassic.

Rhamphorhynchus

Swimming reptiles

Some sea reptiles looked like dolphins or fish. Others had long necks or huge jaws.

Mauisaurus

Mauisaurus

(mou-ee-SORE-us)

One of a group of long-necked sea reptiles called plesiosaurs (PLEE-see-o-saws). May have flapped flippers up and down like sea turtles. Quick neck movements helped catch fish. 12m (40ft) long. Late Cretaceous.

Nothosaurus

Nothosaurus

(no-tho-SORE-us)

Early sea reptile. Caught fish with sharp teeth. Webbed feet for swimming. 3m (10ft) long. Triassic.

Liopleurodon

(lie-o-PLOO-ro-don)

Largest known member of a group of fierce, short-necked creatures called pliosaurs (PLY-o-saws). Hunted plesiosaurs and other big sea reptiles, sniffing them out with powerful sense of smell. 15m (50ft) long. Late Jurassic.

Ichthyosaurus

Ichthyosaurus

(ik-thee-o-SORE-us)

Dolphin-like shape. Gave birth to live young. Swam like a fish, lashing tail from side to side. Used its fins to balance and steer through water. 1.8m (6ft) long. Early Jurassic.

Liopleurodon

Survivors

65 million years ago, a mysterious disaster killed all dinosaurs, pterosaurs and sea reptiles. Many of the animals that survived were mammals (animals that feed their babies with milk, and have warm bodies and hair).

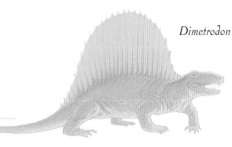
Dimetrodon

Cynognathus

Dimetrodon

(dim-EAT-rod-on)

Early ancestor of mammals. Tall spines made a sail shape on its back. It may have displayed this when trying to attract a mate or threaten enemies. Sharp teeth. 3m (10ft) long. Permian.

Cynognathus

(sy-nog-NAITH-us)

Some mammal-like features, including several different types of teeth. Dog-like look. 2m (6½ft) long. Early Triassic.

Thrinaxodon

Megazostrodon

Megazostrodon

(mega-ZOST-ro-don)

One of the earliest true mammals. Experts think it was hairy and fed its babies on its milk. Tiny and shrew-like. Hunted at night for insects and grubs. 8–10cm (3–4in) long. Early Jurassic.

Thrinaxodon

(thrin-AX-o-don)

Even more mammal-like than *Cynognathus*. Different kinds of teeth, and whiskers on nose. May even have had hairy body, but not yet any evidence for this. 50cm (20in) long. Early Triassic.

Smilodon

(SMILE-o-don)

Lived about 11,000 years ago, during
the last ice age. Fierce; hunted
other mammals such as horses and
camels. 3m (10ft) long. Neogene.

Woolly mammoth

Smilodon

Woolly mammoth

Lived during the last ice age. Kept warm
by its woolly coat and a thick layer of fat.
Remains have been found in the permafrost
(permanently frozen ground) of Siberia in
Russia. 6.5m (21ft) long. Neogene.

Archaeopteryx

(ark-ee-OP-ter-ix)

Probably the first bird. Related to
dinosaurs such as *Velociraptor*. May not
have flown like modern bird. Could have
flapped wings, but not strongly enough
to take off from ground. 20cm (8in)
long. Late Jurassic.

Archaeopteryx

*Archaeopteryx
fossil*

Archaeopteryx fossil

The first *Archaeopteryx* fossil was
found in 1861. The feathers on the
wings and tail can be seen very
clearly. It had teeth, a long bony
tail, and wing claws. Its legs were
probably covered with scaly skin, like
dinosaurs and some modern birds.

Index and checklist

This list will help you find every dinosaur and prehistoric animal in the book. The first number after each entry tells you which page it is on. The second is the sticker number.

Cover design: Marc Maynard
Digital imaging: Keith Furnival
American editor: Carrie Armstrong

Cover photograph © Kokoro/NHMPL
This edition first published in 2010 by Usborne Publishing Ltd, Usborne House, 83–85 Saffron Hill, London ECIN 8RT, England.
www.usborne.com Copyright © 2010, 1980 Usborne Publishing Ltd. The name Usborne and the devices ♀♥ are Trade Marks of Usborne Publishing Ltd. All rights reserved. No part of this publication may be reproduced, stored in a retrieval system, or transmitted in any form or by any means, electronic, mechanical, photocopying, recording or otherwise, without the prior permission of the publisher. UE. First printed in America in 2010. Printed in Heshan, Guangdong, China.